THAT'S A GOOD TUNE! BOOK 2

MUSIC BY

MALCOLM ARCHER
JOHN DANKWORTH
ANDREW GANT
MAX HARRIS
RICHARD LLOYD
BETTY ROE
MIKE SAMMES
CHRISTOPHER TAMBLING
NORMAN WARREN

ILLUSTRATIONS BY
ROY MITCHELL

Kevin
Mayhew

We hope you enjoy *That's a Good Tune* Book 2.
Further copies of this and the other books in the series
are available from your local music shop.

In case of difficulty, please contact the publisher direct:

The Sales Department
KEVIN MAYHEW LTD
Rattlesden
Bury St Edmunds
Suffolk IP30 0SZ

Phone 0449 737978
Fax 0449 737834

Please ask for our complete catalogue of outstanding Instrumental Music.

First published in Great Britain in 1994 by Kevin Mayhew Ltd

© Copyright 1994 Kevin Mayhew Ltd

ISBN 0 86209 551 4
Catalogue No: 3611123

Music Editor: Anthea Smith
Music setting by Louise Hill

Printed and bound in Great Britain

CONTENTS

ABOUT THE COMPOSERS

Malcolm Archer, sometime cocktail bar pianist, is an international organist and recently gave a recital on the largest organ in the world at Wanamaker's Department Store in Philadelphia. He appears frequently on the BBC2 programme *The Organist Entertains* and was organ soloist on the recording *Classic Rock Symphonies* with the London Symphony Orchestra.

John Dankworth is the ultimate all-round musician: jazzman playing with all the greatest names from Dizzy Gillespie to Sarah Vaughan; prolific composer of film scores, choral and orchestral works; conductor of symphony orchestras worldwide; and educationalist. In addition to all this he has the good fortune to be married to the singer Cleo Laine.

Andrew Gant is a singer, pianist, conductor and arranger, working with such famous vocal groups as The Tallis Scholars, The Sixteen and the choir of Westminster Abbey. He is musical director of the Light Blues, with whom he has toured all over the world, and the Thursford Christmas concerts which regularly attract an audience of over 70,000. And, if that's not a busy enough life, he is also Director of Music in Chapel at Selwyn College, Cambridge.

Max Harris has won two Ivor Novello awards for *The Gurney Slade* theme and *The Kipling Stories* theme. He is also the composer of numerous other theme tunes, including *Porridge, Open All Hours* and *Poldark 2*. As musical director he was responsible for several LP's featuring Yehudi Menuhin and Stephane Grapelli.

Richard Lloyd had a youthful ambition to be a (respectable) night club pianist in Paris. When that didn't work out he became Organist of Durham Cathedral instead, and has since followed a distinguished career as a church musician and composer of choral music. He is especially interested in writing music for young players.

Betty Roe is a cabaret artiste, wizz piano player and composer. She studied at the Royal Academy of Music and later with the famous British composer Lennox Berkeley. Her musicals for schools bear her trade marks of wit and humour.

Mike Sammes is the founder of the famous Mike Sammes singers, who have worked with hundreds of major artists including Cliff Richard, Andy Williams, The Beatles, Tom Jones, Barbara Streisand – the list is endless. They have also issued a string of successful solo albums of their own and were recently awarded BASCA's Gold Badge for services to British music.

Christopher Tambling is Director of Music at Glenalmond College in Perth, Scotland. He plays organ and harpsichord and conducts the Perth Symphony Orchestra. When he is not composing he likes to cook and make wine. His recent musical *Singing, Dancing Carpenter,* co-authored with Michael Forster, is enjoying enormous success.

Norman Warren used to play the great Wurlitzer organ at the Trocadero in London's Elephant and Castle (he was paid ten shillings a session – fifty pence in today's money) and he once played for Diana Dors. Now, as Archdeacon of Rochester, he is more concerned with church organs and is a prolific composer of hymns and choral music.

RUNAWAY TRAIN

by MALCOLM ARCHER

THREE MEN IN A BOAT

by MIKE SAMMES

Gently rocking ($\dot{}$ = 84)

For Sarah

HIPPY HABANERA

by BETTY ROE

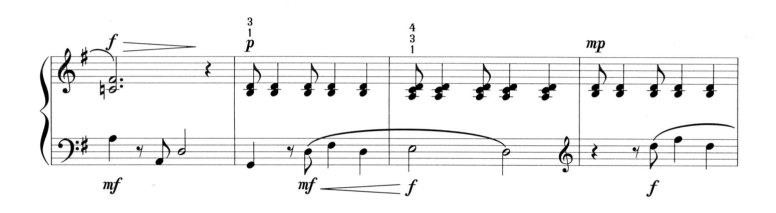

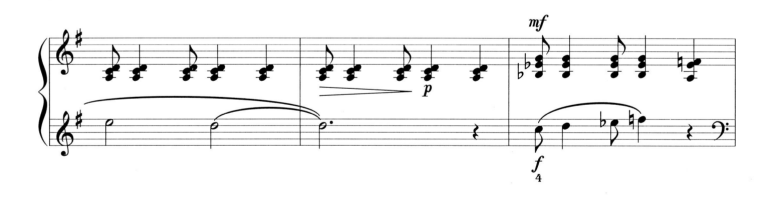

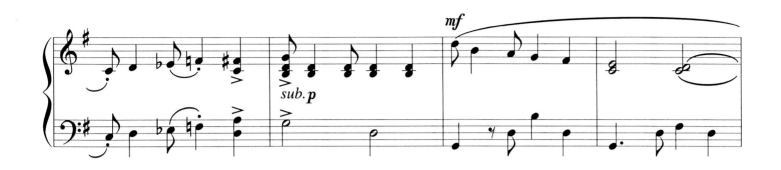

JIM KNOBBLY KNEES

by MAX HARRIS

Slowly and gently

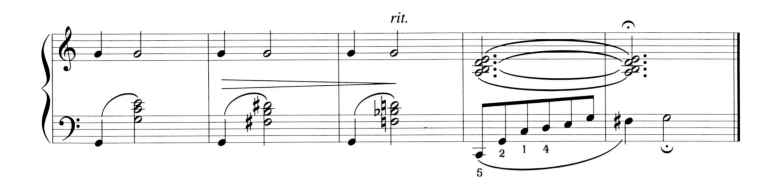

DOLLY'S DOODLES
by ANDREW GANT

Allegro - jauntily

JOSHUA'S DREAM

by NORMAN WARREN

For Benjamin

HAGGIS HUNTING

by CHRISTOPHER TAMBLING

LULLABY FOR LULU

by MAX HARRIS

Slow and gentle (♩ = c.66)

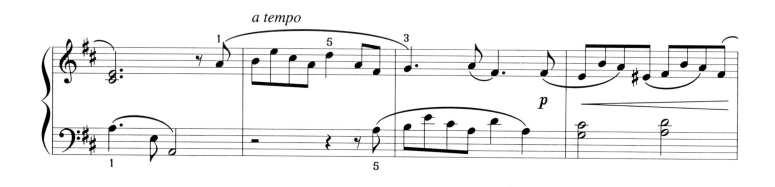

TREE HOUSE

by JOHN DANKWORTH

Andantino ($\quarternote$ = 120)

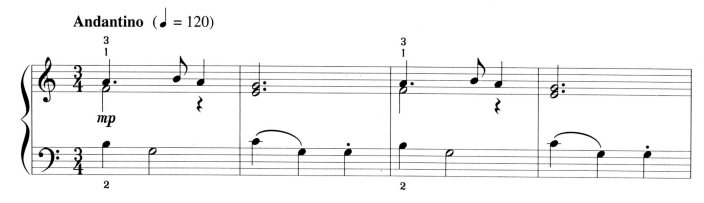

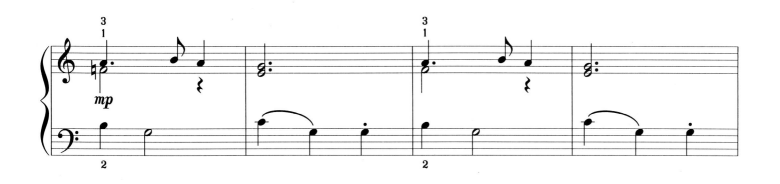

WARM ICE CREAM

by MALCOLM ARCHER

Smoothly flowing (♪ = 132)

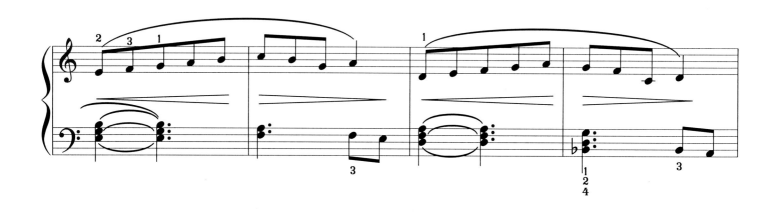

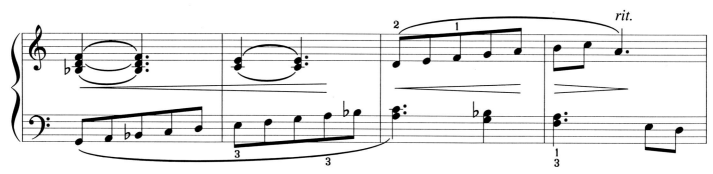

IN DAYS OF OLD

by MIKE SAMMES

LOST LULLABY

by ANDREW GANT

Gentle waltz tempo

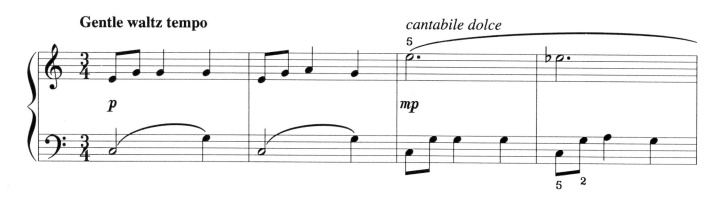

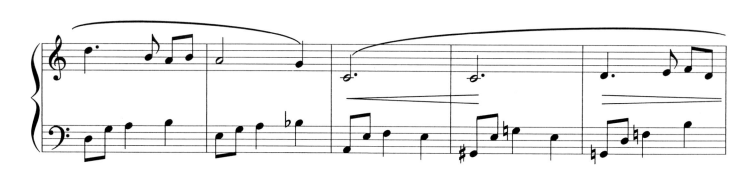

LAZY BONES

by MALCOLM ARCHER

Slow with feeling (♩ = 80)

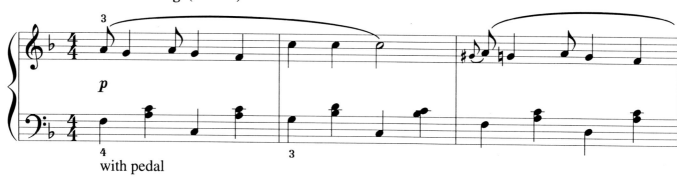

with pedal

Ped.

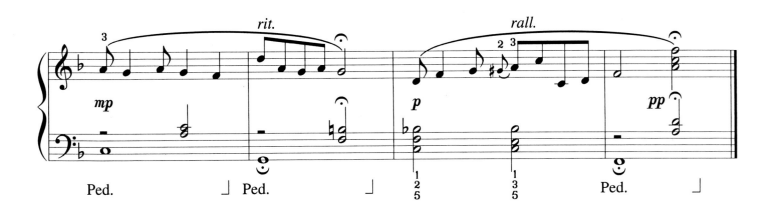

STRUDEL STROLL

by RICHARD LLOYD